This
Treasure Cove Story
belongs to

WINNIE-THE-POOH
AND TIGGER

A CENTUM BOOK 978-1-912396-47-4
Published in Great Britain by Centum Books Ltd.
This edition published 2018.
1 3 5 7 9 10 8 6 4 2

Centum Books Ltd, 20 Devon Square, Newton Abbot,
Devon, TQ12 2HR, UK.

www.centumbooksltd.co.uk | books@centumbooksltd.co.uk
CENTUM BOOKS Limited Reg. No. 07641486.

A CIP catalogue record for this book is available
from the British Library.

Printed in China.

A Treasure Cove Story

Winnie-the-Pooh
AND TIGGER

Pictures by
WALT DISNEY STUDIOS

R_{oo's} mum, Kanga, had a very busy morning ahead of her. She had lots of jobs to do, so she made Roo and Tigger some tasty sandwiches and sent them off for a fun morning in the forest.

    As Roo and Tigger hopped and skipped through the forest,
Roo wanted to hear all about the things that Tiggers do.
    'Can Tiggers fly?' asked Roo.
    'Of course,' said Tigger, 'They're very good flyers, but
they don't like to do it much.'
    'Why ever not?' said Roo.
    'They just don't.' replied Tigger.
    'If I could fly I would fly all the time.' said Roo.
Tigger told him that was because he wasn't a Tigger.

'How about jumping?' said Roo, 'Can they jump high like Kangas?'

'Why yes,' said Tigger. 'But only when they want to.'

Roo loved to jump and challenged Tigger to a jumping competition.

'I am sure I would win,' said Tigger. 'But we had better keep going as we don't want to be late.'

'Late for what?' asked Roo.

But Tigger didn't answer as he was too busy hurrying ahead.

After hurrying along for a while, they came to the Six Pine Trees.
'Oooh, I can swim,' said Roo. 'I love to swim. Can Tiggers swim?'
'Of course they can, Tiggers can do everything.'

'How about climbing? Can they climb tall trees better than Poohs?' asked Roo.
Tigger smiled and said bravely, 'Oh yes, Tiggers are great at climbing. Jump on my back and I will show you that Tiggers can climb much better than Poohs.'

Roo hopped up and down. He was very excited. Tigger felt very confident that of all the things he had said Tiggers could do, climbing would be the easiest.

So Roo jumped onto Tigger's back and Tigger began to climb the tall tree.

He climbed up the tall tree trunk… higher and higher.
'See,' Tigger said. 'I told you Tiggers could climb trees.'
And up Tigger climbed… higher and higher.
'It's not easy though,' Tigger told Roo. 'Then of course,
you have to climb back down, which isn't easy either.'
And then Tigger stopped.

'Why have you stopped?' said Roo.

'Well… erm… to look over there. At the nice view.'
replied Tigger, carefully resting his paws on a branch
and trying not to look down.

CRACCCCKKKK!

Suddenly the branch Tigger was standing on broke.
Tigger only just managed to hang onto the branch above
him, and Roo only just managed to hang onto Tigger!

Very carefully Tigger managed to swing his back paw, then his other back paw up and over the branch he was dangling from, until finally he was sitting on it.

Roo climbed off Tigger's back and sat down next to him.

'Why have we stopped here, are we at the top?'

'No,' said Tigger.

'Shall we keep going till we reach the top?' said Roo.

'No,' said Tigger, wishing he had gone for a swim instead.

'Shall we climb down?' said Roo.

Tigger shook his head.

'I'm hungry,' said Roo. 'Are you?'

Tigger nodded.

'Where are our sandwiches?' asked Roo.

Tigger looked down, then suggested they wait a while.

They waited and they waited.
Finally, they spotted Pooh and Piglet
walking in the forest below.
'Oooh! Look! Pooh… Piglet…' shouted Roo.

'Pooh!' cried Piglet. 'It's Tigger and Roo!'
'So it is,' said Pooh.
'Tigger and Roo!' called Piglet. 'What are
you doing up such a very tall tree?'

'We can't get down!'
cried Roo. 'We're just like
Owl living in a tree. I don't
think we'll ever come down.'

'How did you get up there?' asked Piglet.
'I hopped on Tigger's back,' said Roo. 'Then
Tigger climbed all the way up here. But he doesn't
seem to want to climb all the way down, so we've
decided to stop here.'

'Oh dear,' said Pooh, 'what shall we do?'
'Are they stuck?' asked Piglet.
Pooh nodded and sat down to eat Roo's sandwiches.

'I suppose I could climb up and bring Roo down on my
back,' said Pooh, chewing slowly, 'but Tigger is too big for
me to carry, so we'll have to think of something else to do.'

And while he thought about it, he
began to eat Tigger's sandwiches, too.

Pooh thought and he chewed… and he thought
and he chewed some more. And just as he took his last
mouthful of sandwich, who should come strolling along
but Christopher Robin and Eeyore.

'Hey, there's Pooh!' said Christopher Robin,
'Hello Pooh. Are you and Piglet having a picnic?'

'Oh Pooh. Look! It's Christopher Robin!' said Piglet.
'And Eeyore,' said Eeyore.
'Tigger and Roo are stuck up a tree.' Pooh told him.
'Can you think of something to do?' asked Piglet.
Christopher Robin stared upwards and tried to think
of something to do.

'Perhaps,' suggested Piglet, 'Pooh can stand on Eeyore's back, then I can stand on Pooh's back and we can reach…'

'My back will break!' Eeyore told them.

'Well we can't do that then,' said Pooh.

'I've got an idea!' cried Christopher Robin suddenly.

'I'll take off my shirt,' said Christopher Robin, 'and then perhaps if we all hold a bit of it, we can create a soft and bouncy landing for Roo and Tigger to jump into.'

'That sounds like a good idea,' said Eeyore. 'Let's try and get everyone down without anyone – or anyone's back – getting hurt.'

When they told Roo their plan, he was very excited.
'Oooh! Tigger! We're going to jump! Can Tigger's jump
downwards? I expect so, as it's a bit like flying. Here I go.
Look at me, Tigger, look at me! WEEE-HEEEEE!'

Roo jumped, fell and bounced onto Christopher Robin's shirt. He was going so fast, he bounced straight back up. Roo squealed with excitement and bounced up and down for quite some time… until he finally stopped.

'Your turn Tigger,' Roo called out. 'It's so much fun!'

Tigger looked down at Roo and wondered if Tiggers could jump and, more importantly, bounce as well as Kangas. How he wished he had gone swimming instead of climbing the tall tree.

'Come on,' called Christopher Robin. 'You'll be fine.' Tigger wondered if it would help if he closed his eyes.

He thought it might, so Tigger did just that and closed his eyes tight. He jumped and fell… but Tigger did not bounce.

'Arghhh!' Tigger shouted as he dropped from the tree.

'Ouch!' shouted the others as Tigger thumped into them, tearing Christopher Robin's shirt and knocking everyone to the ground.

Christopher Robin, Pooh and Piglet picked themselves up, then they pulled Tigger up and finally poor Eeyore, too.

'Oh dear!' said Christopher Robin. 'Eeyore, are you hurt?'

Eeyore said nothing for a long time. And then he said:
'I am not hurt. But what about Tigger?'

Tigger was already back to his old self again. Christopher
Robin smiled, 'Tiggers are good at lots of things but what they
really do best is bounce back quickly.'

Treasure Cove Stories

Book list may be subject to change.